P9-CLS-597

HOUGHTON MIFFLIN
The Literature Experience
READING

Celebrate Reading with us!

Cover and Title Page Illustrations by Anne Kennedy.

Acknowledgments appear on page 150.

Copyright © 1993 by Houghton Mifflin Company. All rights reserved.

No part of this work may be reproduced or transmitted in any form or by any means, electronic or mechanical, including photocopying and recording, or by any information storage or retrieval system without the prior written permission of the copyright owner, unless such copying is expressly permitted by federal copyright law. With the exception of nonprofit transcription in Braille, Houghton Mifflin is not authorized to grant permission for further uses of copyrighted selections reprinted in this text without the permission of their owners. Permission must be obtained from the individual copyright owners as identified herein. Address requests for permission to make copies of Houghton Mifflin material to School Permissions, Houghton Mifflin Company, One Beacon Street, Boston, MA 02108.

Printed in the U.S.A.

ISBN: 0-395-61545-3

123456789-D-96 95 94 93 92

Me, Myself, and I

Senior Author
John J. Pikulski

*Senior Coordinating
Author*
J. David Cooper

*Senior Consulting
Author*
William K. Durr

Coordinating Authors
Kathryn H. Au
M. Jean Greenlaw
Marjorie Y. Lipson
Susan E. Page
Sheila W. Valencia
Karen K. Wixson

Authors
Rosalinda B. Barrera
Edwina Bradley
Ruth P. Bunyan
Jacqueline L. Chaparro
Jacqueline C. Comas
Alan N. Crawford
Robert L. Hillerich
Timothy G. Johnson
Jana M. Mason
Pamela A. Mason
William E. Nagy
Joseph S. Renzulli
Alfredo Schifini

Senior Advisor
Richard C. Anderson

Advisors
Christopher J. Baker
Charles Peters
MaryEllen Vogt

HOUGHTON MIFFLIN COMPANY   BOSTON

Atlanta   Dallas   Geneva, Illinois   Palo Alto   Princeton   Toronto

THEME 1

10

Me, Myself, and I

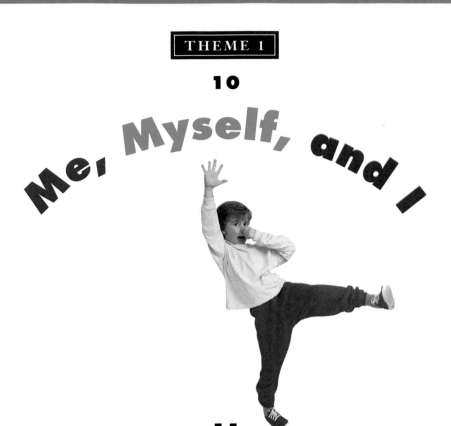

11

In the Mirror
a poem
by Merlin Millet

14

❧ Here Are My Hands
by Bill Martin Jr. and John Archambault

40

❧ The Things I Do
a poem
by Karla Kuskin

❧ Award Winner

42

If You're Happy and You Know It
a traditional song

56

When I Am . . .
a fingerplay
by Liz Cromwell and Dixie Hibner

58

Changing
a poem
by Mary Ann Hoberman

BIG BOOK

A Mouse in My House
by Nancy Van Laan

THEME 2

60

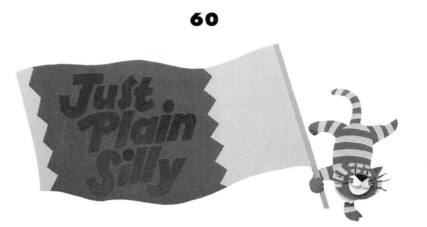

Just Plain Silly

61

The Purple Cow
a poem
by Gelett Burgess

64

Paco and the Taco
by Maxine S. Durán

82

Three Ghostesses
a traditional poem

83

A Matter of Taste
a poem
by Eve Merriam

84

The Ants Go Marching
a traditional song

96.

✦ Ants Live Here
a poem
by Lilian Moore

📖

BIG BOOK
✦ My Perfect Neighborhood
by Leah Komaiko

 THEME 3

98

CHANGES,

CHANGES

99

The Wish
a poem
by Ann Friday

102

The Very Hungry Caterpillar
by Eric Carle

126

Fuzzy Wuzzy, Creepy Crawly
a poem
by Lillian Schulz

127

Every Week Song
a poem
by Myra Cohn Livingston

128

☆ Leo the Late Bloomer
by Robert Kraus

148

☆ Big
a poem
by Dorothy Aldis

149

Something About Me
a traditional rhyme

📖

BIG BOOK
An Egg Is An Egg
by Nicki Weiss

THEME 1

ME, MYSELF, and I

10

IN THE MIRROR

In the mirror
I can see
that I'm
not one,
but I am
three.
The mirror
is the place
to see
I,
    Myself,
        And Me.

by Merlin Millet

11

A Mouse in My House

by Nancy Van Laan

This book is about a boy who has a wriggly mouse in his house, a scraggly ape, a clumsy lion, and a grumbly bear! When you read the story together, you'll find out about the boy and his zoo. Maybe there's a zoo in your house, too!

Me, Myself, and I

14

Here Are My Hands

by Bill Martin Jr. and John Archambault

illustrated by Ted Rand

42

If You're Happy and You Know It

a traditional song

13

Here Are My Hands

by **Bill Martin Jr.** and **John Archambault**
illustrated by **Ted Rand**

Award Winner

Here are my hands
for catching and throwing.

Here are my feet
for stopping and going.

18

Here is my head
for thinking and knowing.

Here is my nose
for smelling and blowing.

22

23

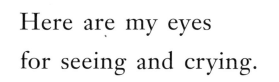

Here are my eyes
for seeing and crying.

Here are my ears
for washing and drying.

Here are my knees
for falling down.

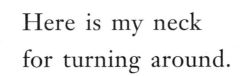

Here is my neck
for turning around.

Here are my cheeks
for kissing and blushing.

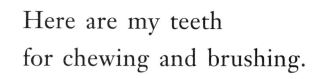

Here are my teeth
for chewing and brushing.

Here is my elbow,
my arm, and my chin.

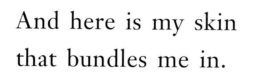

And here is my skin
that bundles me in.

Award Winner

The Things I Do

I'm very good at climbing
I nearly climbed a tree
But just as I was almost up
I sort of skinned my knee.

I'm wonderful at walking
I almost walked a mile
But when I got around the block
I rested for a while.

1 MILE

I'm excellent at swimming
Though I'm not very old
I almost swam the ocean once
But the water was too cold.

But what I'm really best at
Is skipping down the hall.
I'm very good at skipping.
I'm wonderful at skipping.

I'm marvelous at skipping,
That is unless I fall.

by Karla Kuskin

IF HAPPY AND YOU

YOU'RE

a traditional song

KNOW IT

If you're happy and you know it,
   clap your hands.
If you're happy and you know it,
   clap your hands.

If you're happy and you know it,
And you really want to show it . . .

If you're happy and you know it,
   clap your hands!

44

If you're angry and you know it,
  stamp your feet.
If you're angry and you know it,
  stamp your feet.

If you're angry and you know it,
And you really want to show it . . .

If you're angry and you know it,
  stamp your feet!

47

If you're silly and you know it,
 wiggle your nose.
If you're silly and you know it,
 wiggle your nose.

If you're silly and you know it,
And you really want to show it . . .

If you're silly and you know it,
 wiggle your nose!

If you're sad and you know it,
say, "Boo-hoo."
If you're sad and you know it,
say, "Boo-hoo."

If you're sad and you know it,
And you really want to show it . . .

If you're sad and you know it,
say, "Boo-hoo."

If you're tired and you know it,
  go to sleep.
If you're tired and you know it,
  go to sleep.

If you're tired and you know it,
And you really want to show it . . .

If you're tired and you know it,
  go to sleep.

If you're happy and you know it,
   shout, "Hooray!"
If you're happy and you know it,
   shout, "Hooray!"

   If you're happy and you know it,
   And you really want to show it . . .

   If you're happy and you know it,
   shout . . .

When I Am...

When I am sad, I want to cry.
When I am proud, I want to fly.

When I am curious, I want to know.
When I am impatient, I want to go.

When I am bored, I want to play.
When I am happy, I smile all day.

When I am shy, I want to hide.
When I'm unhappy, I stay inside.

When I am puzzled, I want to shrug.
When I am loving, I kiss and hug.

Liz Cromwell
Dixie Hibner

56

57

CHANGING

I know what *I* feel like;
I'd like to be *you*
And feel what *you* feel like
And do what *you* do.
I'd like to change places
For maybe a week
And look like your look-like
And speak as you speak.
And think what you're thinking
And go where you go
And feel what you're feeling
And know what you know.
I wish we could do it;
What fun it would be
If I could try you out
And you could try me.

by Mary Ann Hoberman

Just Plain Silly

The Purple Cow

I never saw a Purple Cow,
   I never hope to see one;
But I can tell you, anyhow,
   I'd rather see than be one.

by Gelett Burgess

BIG BOOK

My Perfect Neighborhood

by Leah Komaiko

As a girl walks through her neighborhood, she sees some very strange and silly things. When you read the story together, think about where you live. Are silly things happening in your neighborhood, too?

My Perfect Neighborhood
by Leah Komaiko
illustrated by Barbara Westman

Just Plain Silly

Paco and the Taco 64
by Maxine S. Durán
translated from Spanish
illustrated by Denise and Fernando

The Ants Go Marching 84
a traditional song
illustrated by Don Stuart

63

Paco and the Taco

by Maxine Durán
translated from Spanish
illustrated by Denise and Fernando

Paco wanted to make a HUGE taco,
the biggest taco EVER!

Paco asked his friends the animals what to do.

Paco asked his friend the toad.
"Toad, Toad, how can I fill my big taco?"

The toad said, "Add beans, BLACK beans."
"Oh yes!" said Paco. "That sounds just fine.
This taco will taste simply divine!"

Paco asked his friend the dog.
"Dog, Dog, how can I fill my big taco?"

The dog said, "Add onion, WHITE onion."
"Oh!" said Paco. "Of course! Why not?
My friend, I think you've hit the spot!"

Paco asked his friend the rabbit.
"Rabbit, Rabbit, how can I fill my big taco?"

The rabbit said, "Add lettuce, GREEN lettuce.
"Oh yes!" said Paco. "That sounds just fine.
This taco will taste simply divine!"

72

Paco asked his friend the bear.
"Bear, Bear, how can I fill my big taco?"

The bear said, "Add salsa, RED salsa."
"Oh!" said Paco. "Of course! Why not?
My friend, I think you've hit the spot!"

Paco asked his friend the cow.
"Cow, Cow, how can I fill my big taco?"

The cow said, "Add cheese, YELLOW cheese.
"Oh yes!" said Paco. "That sounds just fine.
This taco will taste simply divine!"

Then, Paco asked all of his friends.
He asked the toad,
the dog,
the rabbit,
the bear,
and the cow.

"Friends, friends, what else can I use to fill
my taco?"
The animals said, "Nothing else! Let's eat!"

"Oh!" said Paco. "Of course! Why not?
My friends, I think you've hit the spot!"

So Paco and his friends ate an ENORMOUS taco, the BIGGEST taco ever!!!

Three Ghostesses

Three little ghostesses,
Sitting on postesses,
Eating buttered toastesses,
Greasing their fistesses,
Up to their wristesses.
Oh, what beastesses
To make such feastesses!

a traditional rhyme

82

A Matter of Taste

Award Winner

What does your tongue like the most?
Chewy meat or crunchy toast?

A lumpy bumpy pickle or tickly pop?
A soft marshmallow or a hard lime drop?

Hot pancakes or a sherbet freeze?
Celery noise or quiet cheese?

Or do you like pizza
More than any of these?

by Eve Merriam

The Ants Go Marching

a traditional song

illustrated by Don Stuart

The ants go marching
       One by one,
Hoorah! Hoorah!

The ants go marching
       One by one,
Hoorah!   Hoorah!

The ants go marching
       One by one,
The little one stopped
       To have some fun!

And they all go marching,
Down into the ground,
To get out of the rain.

Boom,   boom,
     boom,   boom,

Boom,   boom,
     boom,   boom.

The bees go marching
Two by two,
Hoorah! Hoorah!

The bees go marching
Two by two,
Hoorah!   Hoorah!

The bees go marching
Two by two,
The little one stopped
To tie its shoe!

And they all go marching,
Down into their hive,
To get out of the rain.

Boom,   boom,
boom,   boom,

Boom,   boom,
boom,   boom.

The mice go marching
    Three by three,
Hoorah! Hoorah!

The mice go marching
    Three by three,
Hoorah!   Hoorah!

The mice go marching
    Three by three,
The little one stopped
    To climb a tree!

And they all go marching,
    Down into their nest,
      To get out of the rain.

Boom,   boom,
    boom,   boom,

      Boom,   boom,
        boom,   boom.

The ducks go marching
    Four by four,
Hoorah! Hoorah!

The ducks go marching
    Four by four,
Hoorah!   Hoorah!

The ducks go marching
    Four by four,
The little one stopped
    To knock on a door!

And they all go marching,
    Down into their pond,
        To get out of the rain.

Boom,   boom,
    boom,   boom,

    Boom,   boom,
        boom,   boom.

The rabbits go marching
   Five by five,
Hoorah! Hoorah!

The rabbits go marching
   Five by five,
Hoorah!   Hoorah!

The rabbits go marching
   Five by five,
The little one stopped
   To take a drive!

And they all go marching,
   Down into their hole,
     To get out of the rain.

Boom,   boom,
   boom,   boom,

     Boom,   boom,
       boom,   boom.

The foxes go marching
Six by six,
Hoorah! Hoorah!

The foxes go marching
Six by six,
Hoorah! Hoorah!

The foxes go marching
Six by six,
The little one stopped
To pick up sticks!

And they all go marching,
Down into their den,
To get out of the rain.

Boom,   boom,
boom,   boom,

Boom,   boom,
boom,   boom.

90

The pigs go marching
    Seven by seven,
Hoorah! Hoorah!

The pigs go marching
    Seven by seven,
Hoorah!   Hoorah!

The pigs go marching
    Seven by seven,
The little one stopped
    To count to eleven!

And they all go marching,
    Down into their mud,
        To get out of the rain.

Boom,   boom,
    boom,   boom,

        Boom,   boom,
            boom,   boom.

The sheep go marching
   Eight by eight,
Hoorah! Hoorah!

The sheep go marching
   Eight by eight,
Hoorah!   Hoorah!

The sheep go marching
   Eight by eight,
The little one stopped
   To close the gate!

And they all go marching,
   Down into their barn,
    To get out of the rain.

Boom,   boom,
   boom,   boom,

     Boom,   boom,
       boom,   boom.

The bears go marching
    Nine by nine,
Hoorah! Hoorah!

The bears go marching
    Nine by nine,
Hoorah!   Hoorah!

The bears go marching
    Nine by nine,
The little one stopped
    To swing from a vine!

And they all go marching,
    Down into their cave,
        To get out of the rain.

Boom,   boom,
    boom,   boom,

        Boom,   boom,
            boom,   boom.

They all go marching
    Ten by ten,
Hoorah! Hoorah!

They all go marching
    Ten by ten,
Hoorah!   Hoorah!

They all go marching
    Ten by ten,
The little ones shout,
    "Let's do it again!"

And they all go marching,
    They all go marching,
        To get out of the rain.

Boom,   boom,
        boom,   boom,

    Boom,   boom,
        boom,   boom.

BOOM!

95

Ants Live Here

Ants live here
by the curb stone,
        see?
They worry a lot
about giants like
        me.

by Lilian Moore

THEME 3

CHANGES, CHANGES, CHANGES

98

The Wish

Each birthday wish
I've ever made
Really does come true.
Each year I wish
I'll grow some more
And every year

I

DO!

by Ann Friday

An Egg Is An Egg
by Nicki Weiss

In this book, a boy and his mother watch how things change. An egg becomes a chick, a seed becomes a flower, and a baby becomes a boy. When you read the story together, you'll learn about other things that change, too! Think about some of the things in your world that change, and some that stay the same.

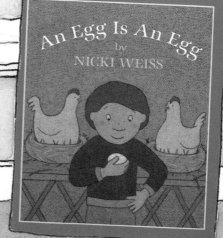

An Egg Is An Egg
by
NICKI WEISS

BIG BOOK

CHANGES, CHANGES, CHANGES

The Very Hungry Caterpillar   102
by Eric Carle

Leo the Late Bloomer   128
by Robert Kraus
illustrated by Jose Aruego

101

THE VERY HUNGRY CATERPILLAR

by Eric Carle

In the light of the moon
a little egg lay on a leaf.

One Sunday morning the warm sun came up and — pop! — out of the egg came a tiny and very hungry caterpillar.

He started to look for some food.

On Monday he ate through one apple.
But he was still hungry.

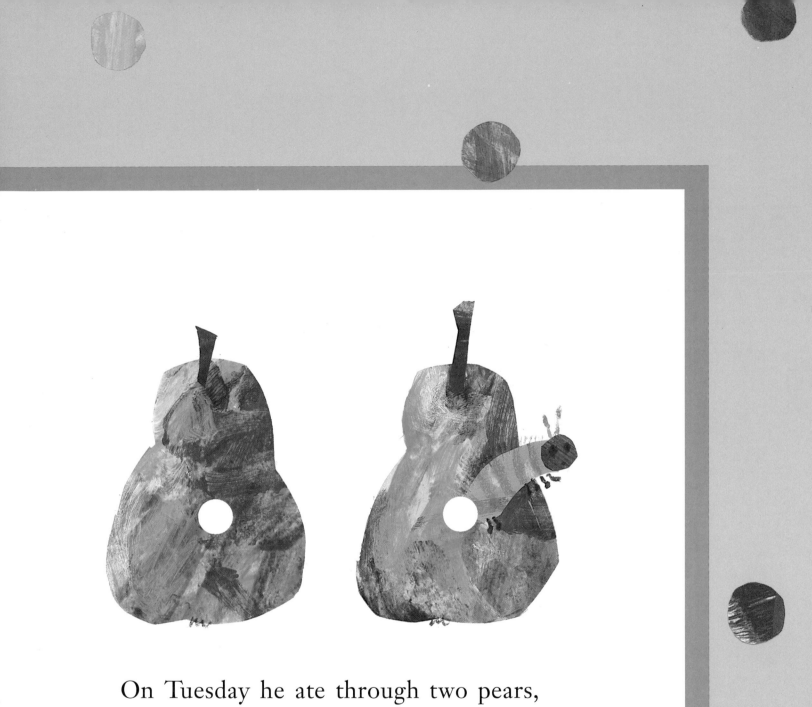

On Tuesday he ate through two pears,
but he was still hungry.

On Wednesday he ate through three plums, but he was still hungry.

On Thursday he ate through four strawberries,
but he was still hungry.

On Friday he ate through five oranges,

but he was still hungry.

On Saturday he ate through

one piece of
chocolate cake,

one ice-cream cone,

one pickle,

one slice of
Swiss cheese,

one slice of salami,

one sausage,

one piece of
cherry pie,

one lollipop,

116

one cupcake,

and one slice of
watermelon.

That night he had a stomachache!

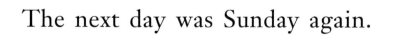

The next day was Sunday again.

The caterpillar ate through
one nice green leaf, and after
that he felt much better.

Now he wasn't hungry
any more *bil* and he wasn't
a little caterpillar any more.
He was a big, fat caterpillar.

He built a small house, called a cocoon,
around himself. He stayed inside
for more than two weeks. Then he
nibbled a hole in the cocoon, pushed
his way out and . . .

he was a beautiful butterfly!

Fuzzy Wuzzy, Creepy Crawly

Fuzzy wuzzy, creepy crawly
  Caterpillar funny,
You will be a butterfly
  When the days are sunny.

Winging, flinging, dancing, springing
  Butterfly so yellow,
You were once a caterpillar,
  Wiggly, wiggly fellow.

by Lillian Schulz

126

Every Week Song

What is the day after Sunday?
Monday.
Tuesday and Wednesday and then
Thursday and
Friday and
Saturday
And then we begin again. . . .

by Myra Cohn Livingston

127

LEO

the LATE BLOOMER

by Robert Kraus • pictures by Jose Aruego

Leo couldn't do anything right.

He couldn't read.

131

He couldn't write.

owl
Elephant
Snake
Plover
Crocodile

132

He couldn't draw.

He was a sloppy eater.

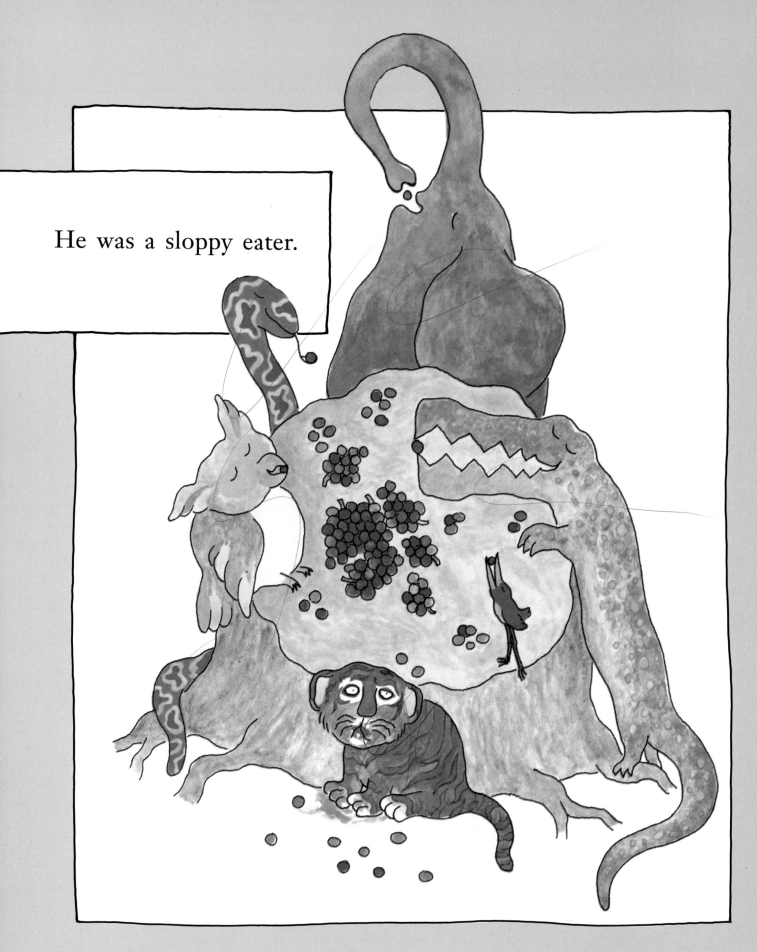

134

And, he never
said a word.

135

"What's the matter with Leo?"
asked Leo's father.
"Nothing," said Leo's mother.
"Leo is just a late bloomer."
"Better late than never,"
thought Leo's father.

Every day Leo's father watched him
for signs of blooming.

And every night Leo's father watched him
for signs of blooming.

"Are you sure Leo's a bloomer?"
asked Leo's father.
"Patience," said Leo's mother,
"A watched bloomer doesn't bloom."

So Leo's father watched television
instead of Leo.

The snows came.
Leo's father wasn't watching.
But Leo still wasn't blooming.

The trees budded.
Leo's father wasn't watching.
But Leo still wasn't blooming.

141

Then one day,
in his own good time,
Leo bloomed!

He could read!

He could write!

He could draw!

He ate neatly!

He also spoke.

And it wasn't just a word.

It was a whole sentence.

And that sentence was . . .

"I made it!"

Big

Now I can catch and throw a ball
And spell
Cat. Dog.
And Pig,
I have finished being small
And started
Being Big.

by Dorothy Aldis

Something About Me

There's something about me
That I'm knowing.
There's something about me
That isn't showing.

I'm growing!

a traditional rhyme

Acknowledgments

For each of the selections listed below, grateful acknowledgment is made for permission to excerpt and/or reprint original or copyrighted material, as follows:

Major Selections

Here Are My Hands, by Bill Martin Jr. and John Archambault, illustrated by Ted Rand. Text copyright © 1985 by Bill Martin Jr. and John Archambault. Illustrations copyright © 1987 by Ted Rand. Reprinted by permission of Henry Holt and Company.

"If You're Happy and You Know It," author unknown. Attempts to locate this rightsholder were unsuccessful. Should the rightsholder see this notice, please contact Houghton Mifflin Company, School Permissions, One Beacon Street, Boston, MA 02108.

Leo the Late Bloomer, by Robert Kraus, illustrated by Jose Aruego. Text copyright © 1971 by Robert Kraus. Illustrations copyright © 1971 by Jose Aruego. Reprinted by permission of HarperCollins Publishers.

The Very Hungry Caterpillar, by Eric Carle. Copyright © 1969 by Eric Carle. Reprinted by permission of Philomel Books.

Poetry

"Ants Live Here," from *I Feel the Same Way* by Lilian Moore. Copyright © 1967 by Lilian Moore. Reprinted by permission of Marian Reiner for the author.

"Big," from *All Together* by Dorothy Aldis. Copyright © 1925-28, 1934, 1939, 1952, renewed 1953-1956, 1962, 1967 by Dorothy Aldis. Reprinted by permission of The Putnam Publishing Group.

"Changing," from *Yellow Butter Purple Jelly Red Jam Black Bread* by Mary Ann Hoberman. Copyright © 1981 by Mary Ann Hoberman. Reprinted by permission of Gina Maccoby Literary Agency.

"Every Week Song," from *Wide Awake and Other Poems* by Myra Cohn Livingston. Copyright © 1959 by Myra Cohn Livingston, renewed 1987. Reprinted by permission of Marian Reiner for the author.

"Fuzzy Wuzzy, Creepy Crawly," by Lillian Schulz, from *Sung Under the Silver Umbrella*, selected by the Literature Committee of the Association for Childhood Education International. Copyright © 1935 by the Association. Reprinted by permission of Lillian Schulz and the Association for Childhood Education International.

"In the Mirror," by Merlin Millet, from *All About Me: Verses I Can Read*, selected by Leland B. Jacobs. Copyright © 1971 by Leland B. Jacobs. Reprinted by permission of Leland B. Jacobs.

"A Matter of Taste," from *Jamboree Rhymes for All Times* by Eve Merriam. Copyright © 1962, 1964, 1966, 1973, 1984 by Eve Merriam. Reprinted by permission of Marian Reiner for the author.

"Something About Me," author unknown. Attempts to locate this rightsholder were unsuccessful. Should the rightsholder see this notice, please contact Houghton Mifflin Company, School Permissions, One Beacon Street, Boston, MA 02108.

"The Things I Do," by Karla Kuskin, from *In the Middle of the Trees*. Copyright © 1986 by Karla Kuskin. Reprinted by permission of the author.

"The Wish," by Ann Friday. Attempts to locate this rightsholder were unsuccessful. Should the rightsholder see this notice, please contact Houghton Mifflin Company, School Permissions, One Beacon Street, Boston, MA 02108.

Others

"When I Am . . . ," from *Finger Frolics* published by Discovery Toys. Compiled by Liz Cromwell, Dixie Hibner, and John R. Faitel. Contributing authors: Rebecca Boynton, Colleen Kobe, Lois Peters, and others. Reprinted by permission of The Partner Press.

Credits

Program Design   Carbone Smolan Associates

Cover Design   Carbone Smolan Associates

Design   **10–149** TextArt

Introduction   (left to right) 1st row: Susan Swan; Denise and Fernando; Ken Karp;   2nd row: Ken Karp; Denise and Fernando; John Lei;   3rd row: Susan Swan; Cyd Moore; Ken Karp;   4th row: Carme Solé Vendrell; Ken Karp; Susan Swan

Table of Contents   **4** Ken Karp;   **6** Susan Swan;   **8** Pau Estrada

Illustration   **10–11** Michelle Dorman;   **14–39** Ted Rand;   **40–41** Nadine Bernard Westcott;   **42–43, 50, 54–55** Michelle Dorman;   **56–57** Carme Solé Vendrell;   **60–63** Susan Swan;   **64–81** Denise and Fernando;   **82–83** Laura Cornell;   **84–95** Don Stuart;   **96–97** Susan Swan;   **98–101** Pau Estrada;   **102–125** Eric Carle;   **126–127** Cyd Moore;   **128–147** Jose Aruego;   **148–149** Pau Estrada

Assignment Photography   **10–13, 42–55, 59** Ken Karp